Do I Need to See the Vet?

For Both Puppies and Adult Dogs

Do I Need to See the Vet?

For Both Puppies and Adult Dogs

Dr. Bob Porter
Dr. Wendy Ing

Macmillan Canada
Toronto

First published in Canada in 2001 by
Macmillan Canada, an imprint of CDG Books Canada Inc.

National Library of Canada Cataloguing in Publication Data

Porter, Bob, 1961–
   Do I need to see the vet? : for both puppies and adult dogs

ISBN 0-55335-011-1

1. Dogs—Wounds and injuries—Treatment—Popular works. 2. Dogs—Diseases—Treatment—Popular works. I. Ing, Wendy. II. Title.

SF991.P67 2001   636.7'0896024   C2001-900645-4

This book is available at special discounts for bulk purchases by your group or organization for sales promotions, premiums, fundraising and seminars. For details, contact: CDG Books Canada Inc., 99 Yorkville Avenue, Suite 400, Toronto, ON, M5R 3K5. Tel: 416-963-8830. Toll Free: 1-877-963-8830. Fax: 416-923-4821. Web site: cdgbooks.com.

1 2 3 4 5 FP 05 04 03 02 01

Conceptualized by Drs. Murat and Stewart
Design concept by Ron Sumners, Sumners Graphics
Text & cover production by Kyle Gell Design
Illustrations by Carl Wiens

Attention
The approach to medical problems is always an evolution. The incorporation of new research, broader clinical knowledge, new technology and new medication may change the best way to manage medical problems. The writers, editors and publisher of this book have made their best effort to create a publication that uses the most up-to-date information available and have given advice that, at the time of publication, would be in accordance with standards of practice. However, in view of human error, changes in medical science or misunderstanding by the reader, neither the writers, publisher nor any other party involved in the preparation or distribution of this publication warrants that information contained herein is in every respect accurate or complete, and they are not responsible for any errors or omissions or for the results obtained from use or misuse of such information. Readers are to be aware that this publication does not at any time replace veterinarians and that people should always seek out a professional opinion if they feel it is warranted.

Macmillan Canada
An imprint of CDG Books Canada Inc.
Toronto

Printed in Canada

For my love, Susan, and our kids, Meghan and Jacob.
And for our dogs past and present, Jesse and Cinder.
Thanks for your ongoing support in my adventures.

— Bob Porter

I would like to dedicate this book to my husband, Randy,
who has supported me through the writing process both
emotionally and technically (I am not a computer whiz),
and to my parents, who have helped me reach my
lifetime goal of becoming a veterinarian.

— Wendy Ing

*The following Registered Trademarks are used in this publication and are identified within using **bold print**.*

Apple Bitter	**Gatorade**	**Pedialyte**	**Skunk-Off**
Aspirin	**Gravol**	**Pepto-Bismol**	**Sunlight**
Benadryl	**Imodium**	**Polysporin**	**Tabasco**
Certs	**Kaopectate**	**Q-tips**	**Tylenol**
Clorets	**Laxatone**	**Quickstop**	**Vicks**
Forbid	**Metamucil**	**Skin-So-Soft**	

Acknowledgments

The authors would like to thank the following for their support:

Dr. Chip Coombs
Dr. Doreen Houston
Jacqueline Ing
Gertrude Porter
Susan Porter
Dr. Brian Murat
Randy Winter
Tim Withey
and Dr. Dianna Wolfe

Table of Contents

LOSS OF APPETITE

VOMITING

DIARRHEA

CONSTIPATION

COUGHING

EAR INFECTIONS

EYE PROBLEMS

SKIN PROBLEMS

LOSS OF APPETITE

VOMITING

DIARRHEA

CONSTIPATION

COUGHING

EAR INFECTIONS

EYE PROBLEMS

SKIN PROBLEMS

Foreword

Learn and laugh as you read this book by Dr. Bob and Dr. Wendy. With a winning combination of experience and humor, they have written an easy-to-read book outlining the common problems of dogs of all ages. From hiccuping to loose poops, you'll learn what's normal and what's not. Complete with illustrations, this book offers some home suggestions for treating your pet and lets you know when it's time to see the veterinarian. The information provided is practical and presented in a way I'm sure you will enjoy—I know I did!

Doreen M. Houston, DVM, DVSc,
Diplomate, ACVIM (Internal Medicine)
Guelph, Ontario, Canada

How to Use This Book

This book has not been written to replace regular visits to your veterinarian. For dogs that have ongoing medical conditions, contact a veterinarian. However, if you just need a little basic advice to get through a camping trip or some of the more common health problems experienced during your dog's lifetime, this is the book for you. The information contained here has been designed to assist you in determining when a condition can be cared for at home versus one that requires prompt veterinary assistance.

To Use This Book Properly:

1. Read the appropriate topic from start to finish before using the advice given.

2. Monitor your dog closely during treatment, making sure to re-evaluate its condition regularly. If the dog is not responding, contact your veterinarian.

3. If at any point your dog appears very ill or its condition worsens, consult your veterinarian.

4. It would be helpful to familiarize yourself with the book's contents BEFORE you need it in an urgent situation.

Medicine Chest for Your Dog

Plan ahead. Have the following items at your finger tips, for treatment at home.

Absorbent cotton

Gauze and bandages

Bandage scissors

Adhesive tape

Tweezers

Hydrogen peroxide

Corn syrup

Laxatone

Cautery powder/Styptic pen

Ice pack

Syringe

Eye flush (contact lens solution)

Ear cleaners

Antihistamine (*Diphenhydramine*—
  Benadryl and others)

ASA (**Aspirin** and others)

Dimenhydrinate (**Gravol** and others)

Bismuth subsalicylate
  (**Pepto-Bismol** and others)

Antibiotic creams
  (**Polysporin** and others)

Cough suppressant
  (*Dextromethorphan* and others)

Rubbing alcohol

Dog toothpaste

Note: Medication should be given based on your dog's size.

Small	< 25 lbs	(< 11 kg)
Medium	25 to 60 lbs	(11 kg to 27 kg)
Large	60 to 100 lbs	(27 kg to 45.5 kg)
Giant	> 100 lbs	(> 45.5 kg)

A general dosage can be calculated based upon a number of mL or mg per kg of weight. However, larger dogs will metabolize medications more slowly than smaller dogs. A maximum dosage should not exceed the recommended human adult dosage on the package.

A rule of thumb:

Small dogs	< 1/2 the child's dose
Medium dogs	= the child's dose
Large / Giant dogs	≤ adult dosage

Although some human medications can be used for your dog, do not experiment. CONSULT YOUR VET.

"An Ounce of Prevention Is Worth a Pound of Cure"

A Guide to Your Dog's Home Physical Exam

Perform an examination of your dog each week at home. You don't have to have a degree in veterinary medicine to do this, you just have to know what your dog looks like when it is healthy. If any changes appear, you can consult the information in this book or your veterinarian.

Where to start?
A good rule of thumb is start at the tip of your dog's nose and work back to the tip of the tail.

Nose
Breathing noises will vary with different breeds—the shorter the snout the more likely it is you will hear more pronounced breathing noises.

Look for:
- Discharge
- Trouble breathing

Teeth
Remember that puppies go through teething around the age of 4 or 5 months. You may notice some bleeding of the gums, loose teeth and increased chewing. Tartar buildup is a more common problem in adult dogs. Routine dental care is the best way to prevent a problem. There are many commercial veterinary dental care products available nowadays, but nothing can fully replace brushing the dog's teeth regularly with a toothpaste designated for pets.

Look for:
- Loose or broken teeth
- Bleeding or raw areas on the gums
- Tartar buildup
- Bad breath

Eyes

Almost all dogs have some discharge from their eyes. Certain breeds have more than others and require a lot of care. Daily washing with a damp cloth may be all that is necessary, but talk to your veterinarian first about correct treatment.

Look for:

- More than normal or greenish discharge
- Redness or cloudiness
- Squinting or avoidance of bright light

Ears

To examine the ears, flip the ear flap back and LOOK WAAAAY DOWN. If any black or yellow debris is visible, it may indicate an infection. If the debris is on the floppy part of the ear it is probably just dirt from playing or digging. Also, have a GOOD SMELL of the ear. Occasionally there is no debris but it smells like dirty socks; this could also be a sign of infection. Regular ear cleaning can be done at home and may be required more frequently in certain breeds.

Look for:

- Redness
- Debris
- Smell
- Scratching / Rubbing ear

Skin/Hair/Coat

Regular grooming (brushing, shaving and baths) may be required more frequently in certain breeds. Most dogs require regular nail trimming in order to prevent injury to the nail or growth into the footpads.

Look for:

- Areas of hair loss
- Areas of red or flaky skin (look between the legs on the belly and just above the tail)
- Lumps or bumps (run your hands all over your dog: don't forget the tail and paws)
- Cuts or scrapes
- Increased scratching

Muscles and Bones

You can examine this area easily by just watching your dog while it is at play or while it is outside going to the bathroom. You can also feel all four legs while examining the dog's skin and hair coat.

Look for:

- Lameness
- Pain
- Swelling or heat

Behavior

Behavior changes can signify health problems. A dog may show its teeth, growl or attempt to bite if you touch something painful. Occasionally dogs will want to be left alone when ill or in pain.

Other Tips

- It is also important to monitor your pet's food and water intake regularly as well as its urination and bowel movements.
- It is important for a veterinarian to perform an immediate physical exam of your dog, and then regular exams once or twice a year, because of the great variation in "normal."

Remember, your dog can't talk. Therefore, it is important that you are observant in order to help your veterinarian make a diagnosis.

Where to Examine Your Dog

There is a reason your vet uses a table to examine your pet, and it is not only to save the vet's back.

A solid table takes your pet out of its normal environment. By placing it on a table for physical examinations, you give it something else to think about and in *most* cases it is easier to handle.

More Tips

- Slow, steady movements
- Soft voice, firm voice when needed

Restraint of Puppies and Dogs

Proper restraint of animals allows veterinarians and animal health care workers to perform their duties and also ensures that both the animal and handler are safe from injury. If a dog feels that the handler is in control, it typically begins to relax and allows treatment.

While administering care to your dog, the most important part of its body to control is the head. In order to properly accomplish this, the dog must be fitted with a nylon or leather collar that allows no more than a **2 to 3 finger space between the collar and the dog.** Loose fitting collars allow the dog to twist around or back away, potentially causing the dog to become free and difficult to handle (not to mention the damage that can occur to your fingers). Choke chains should not be used for restraint during physical exams or during the administration of treatments.

Once you have a good firm hold on the collar, remember the following:

1. **Stand to the side or behind the dog.** Never try to restrain the dog while standing in front of the animal.

2. **Hand positions are important.** If you are standing beside the dog, face the dog's side and grab the collar with the hand closest to the dog's head. For example, if your dog's nose points to the left, use your left hand to grab the collar. If your dog's nose points to the right, use your right hand to grab the collar. This allows you to examine the dog with your free hand, while protecting yourself if the dog decides to turn on you.

3. **Use two people for hard-to-restrain dogs.** One person holds the dog and one person examines the dog and administers the treatments.

- The handler can stand behind the dog and hold the collar with two hands—one on either side of the dog's neck, OR

- From the side of the dog, the handler can reach under the dog's neck, place a "headlock" on the dog and grab the collar on the opposite side. Secure the dog tightly by wrapping the other arm over the back and around the body.

- Remember, even very small dogs are strong for their size; BE FIRM and don't let go.

BEWARE: Dominant Dogs and Fearful Dogs

Some dogs do not like to be restrained and may attempt to bite you. USE COMMON SENSE and do not assume that just because it is your dog, it will not bite you. When dogs are hurt or sick or in pain, there is a higher risk of them biting you. They do not know you are helping and they will be afraid.

Dominant dogs do not like any form of restraint. Go slowly and do not take any unnecessary chances. Rule #1 is DON'T GET BITTEN.

Loss of Appetite

PUPPIES
Possible Signs

- refusal to eat and drink
- swollen abdomen (potbelly)
- vomiting
- lethargy (tired and depressed)

Summary

Loss of appetite or "inappetance" is a serious clinical sign observed in puppies. Loss of appetite can be the result of a variety of conditions both serious and minor, but can lead to life-threatening conditions.

PUPPIES MUST EAT TO SURVIVE, and the smaller and younger the puppy the more important that it eats regularly. Puppies need glucose (sugar) from food for brain fuel. (As dogs get older they can metabolize glucose from fats and proteins contained within their own bodies.)

Puppies may stop eating for a wide variety of reasons, ranging from a sudden change in brands of food to viral infections, to eating the dog owner's shoe.

Loss of Appetite

Puppies

Is your pup less than 10 weeks old?

or

Is your pup depressed or lethargic?　　　**YES** ▶ **CALL YOUR VET**

or

Is your pup bloated?

 NO

Is your pup constipated (not pooping)?　　**YES** ▶ See **CONSTIPATION IN PUPPIES**, page 17.

 NO

Is your pup vomiting?　　**YES** ▶ See **VOMITING IN PUPPIES**, page 10.

 NO

Is your pup drinking ?　　**NO** ▶ **CALL YOUR VET**

 YES

Will your pup eat small amounts of appetizing food, or corn syrup in water (see HOME SUGGESTIONS)?　　**NO** ▶ **CALL YOUR VET**

YES

Tempt your pup with other types or brands of food.

 *Puppies must eat to survive. If a puppy will not eat, **CALL YOUR VET IMMEDIATELY**.*

Home Suggestions

1. Ensure that your pup has been to see the veterinarian and has been checked for intestinal parasites.

2. Give your puppy **small amounts** (1tsp or 5 mL) of a 50:50 mixture of corn syrup and water. This will provide the necessary glucose for brain fuel.

3. Tempt your puppy with small amounts (1 tbsp or 15 mL) of appetizing food (chicken, hamburger, rice or boiled potatoes). Warming the food or adding flavor-enhancing products like garlic powder and ketchup helps make the food more appetizing.

   - If your puppy does eat sporadically, check the food that you have been feeding your puppy and consider changing it.

4. If your puppy is vomiting, observe and record the vomit. Also, check any feces. Look for bits of blood, plastic, cloth, and basically, everything but the kitchen sink. This is very useful information for your veterinarian and will guide the vet towards the correct diagnostic tests (x rays, blood work, fecal exams, etc.)

5. Record the length of time since the puppy has last eaten. Ask all family members and neighbors if the puppy has been fed by someone. Many cases of loss of appetite can be traced to the puppy finding an alternative source of food. If your puppy is still playful and active, you should consider this possibility.

Vomiting

PUPPIES
Possible Signs

:: vomiting (throwing up)

And some or all of the following:

:: loss of appetite (not eating)

:: diarrhea (loose poop) or constipation (not pooping)

:: swollen abdomen (potbelly)

:: painful abdomen

Summary

Remember two principles: puppies eat everything (good and bad) and all puppies vomit (throw up). Veterinarians are asked every day about how to deal with a vomiting puppy. Sudden dietary changes and dietary indiscretion (it ate something that it wasn't supposed to) are the most common causes of vomiting. Usually a puppy will vomit and feel better; however, there are more serious causes of vomiting: foreign-body obstruction (e.g., the plastic toy it ate got stuck); a viral infection; a parasite infection or a gastric accident (twisted stomach, etc.). When affected by a more serious condition, it is important to seek veterinary attention **immediately**.

Puppies do not have the ability to withstand long periods of vomiting. The degree of danger associated with repeated vomiting varies with the size and age of your puppy. The smaller and/or younger the pup, the more quickly you should seek help. If your puppy is depressed or obviously in distress, take it to the vet. If the pup remains bright and alert after vomiting, simply keep a close watch for signs of distress.

To protect your puppy's health, it is important to have your puppy vaccinated and checked for intestinal worms by your veterinarian.

Vomiting

Puppies

 Puppies must eat frequently and cannot withstand long periods without food. Don't wait too long before calling your vet.

Is your pup vomiting blood or digested blood (black and looks like coffee grounds)?

or

Has your pup had bouts of prolonged or repeated vomiting?

YES → **CALL YOUR VET**

 NO

Is your pup bloated (very large belly)?

YES → Check for intestinal worms in the vomit. If not present, see **CONSTIPATION IN PUPPIES**, page 17, then return to this page. If present, **CALL YOUR VET**

NO

Is it possible that there is poison in the vomit (mouse, slug bait, etc.; the vomit might be blue or green)?

YES → **CALL YOUR VET**

NO

Are there foreign bodies in the vomit (bones, sticks, kitchen sinks, etc.)?

YES → **CALL YOUR VET**

NO

Does your pup feel better after vomiting?

NO → **CALL YOUR VET**

YES

use HOME SUGGESTIONS

Is there prolonged vomiting (for 24 hours)?

YES → **CALL YOUR VET**

NO

Monitor for additional vomiting.

Home Suggestions

1. Take your puppy to the vet for its regular puppy visits (vaccines and fecal exam) before your puppy gets sick. Prevention is the best medicine.

2. Before cleaning up the vomit, examine it and try to determine the cause of the vomiting (use something such as a stick to stir it up). Look for: plastic, bone fragments, pieces of wood, cloth and just about anything else you can think of.

3. Ask yourself and family members the following questions:
   - Did you change the brand of puppy food or buy a new bag of food?
   - Did you give the puppy some treats or bones recently?
   - Has your puppy been outside or visiting neighbors without your supervision?
   - Has your puppy just eaten a very large amount of food?

   The above questions and your own observations will typically reveal the cause of the vomiting and you can act accordingly.

4. Simple treatment: Use this treatment when the puppy appears normal and you believe the cause to be dietary indiscretion ("garbage guts," as we say in the trade). In most cases the pup recovers quickly after vomiting.
   - Withhold food and allow the digestive tract time to recover. **Do not withhold a puppy's food for more than a few hours during the day.**
   - Try to give the puppy *very small* amounts of water and monitor for additional vomiting.
   - Use a soothing diet of :
     - Cooked hamburger and cooked rice (50:50); *or*
     - Cooked hamburger and boiled potatoes (50:50)
   - Feed very small amounts of food to the pup, frequently, for example:
     - Day 1: 1 tbsp (15 mL) every hour
   - As the pup recovers (the next day), increase the amount and decrease the frequency:
     - Day 2: 2 to 3 tbsp (45 mL) every 2 hours
     - Adjust volumes and frequency according to the size of your dog

- Once the pup appears to be recovering, start mixing your usual puppy food in with the soothing diet. (Some pups resist the return to the old puppy food because the soothing diet is "just so darn good." Be firm or you will be cooking for your pup forever.)

5. It is common to notice diarrhea following a bout of vomiting. Examining the stool will sometimes reveal the initial cause of your pup's problems. Diarrhea that contains blood (blood can appear bright red, black and tarry, or like strawberry jam) should be investigated by your veterinarian. Some cases of viral diarrhea and vomiting are life threatening; **DO NOT** "wait and see."

6. Evidence of serious cases of vomiting:
   - Prolonged, repeated vomiting that leaves your puppy depressed or in distress
   - Swollen abdomen (usually on the left side of the dog; look at the dog from a few feet away and watch for asymmetry)
   - Depression and listlessness
   - Digested blood (black and looks like coffee grounds)

   If the puppy remains bright, alert, playful and hungry, keep your eye on it. For all serious cases or suspected serious cases of vomiting, **CALL YOUR VET** immediately.

Diarrhea

PUPPIES
Possible Signs

- watery or loose bowel movements
- increased frequency of bowel movements (accidents or "messes" in house)
- may see secondary changes: blood in stool or black stools; reduced appetite; depression; vomiting

Summary

We must keep in mind that puppies like to chew their way through the first months of their lives. It is common to see cases of diarrhea related to dietary indiscretion ("garbage guts"). Puppies that are not vaccinated can get diarrhea due to viruses (*parvovirus*). Intestinal worms are also quite common in young puppies. Most cases of diarrhea will resolve on their own within several days if we are patient. In some cases, however, it can be very serious. One very important thing to remember is that puppies with diarrhea are losing a lot of fluid from their bodies. Therefore, extra care must be taken to make sure that dehydration does not develop.

Diarrhea

Puppies

Has the diarrhea been present for 2 to 3 days?

or

Is your pup depressed or lethargic?

or

Are there signs of abdominal pain
(hunched and whining) or bloating?

YES → **CALL YOUR VET**

 NO

Is your pup vomiting? — **YES** → See **VOMITING IN PUPPIES**, page 10, then return to this page.

 NO

Has your pup been dewormed or checked
for intestinal parasites? — **NO** → **CALL YOUR VET**

 YES

Is there blood in the diarrhea? — **YES** → **CALL YOUR VET**

 NO

Have you changed your pup's diet recently?

or

Has your pup eaten something it shouldn't have (toys,
underwear, shoes, rocks, etc.)?

or

Is your pup getting a lot of human food?

 YES

use HOME SUGGESTIONS

Monitor your pup closely for changes.

*Prolonged diarrhea can be
life threatening to a puppy.
Puppies can very quickly
become weak from dehydra-
tion or low blood sugar.
If concerned, **CALL YOUR VET**.*

Home Suggestions

1. Puppies are more prone to low blood sugar; therefore, do not withhold food the way we do with adult dogs suffering from diarrhea.

2. Giving more frequent but smaller meals using a soothing diet may help (just like chicken soup, when you have the flu). Some suggestions include boiled rice, potatoes, macaroni and lean chicken. Try to avoid foods that are high in fat or contain lactose (milk, cheese). It is not true that puppies need to have milk in their diet. As stools start to firm up, gradually mix in small amounts of your puppy's regular diet. Usually within 4 to 5 days your puppy will be back to eating its own food.

3. Make sure your puppy is getting lots of fresh water, since diarrhea can often lead to dehydration. Some people also like to use electrolyte solutions, such as **Pedialyte** and **Gatorade.**

4. Caution should be taken with puppies regarding medication use (see **Diarrhea in Adult Dogs**, page 43). **Medications should not be used unless prescribed by a vet.**

5. To protect the puppy from infectious diseases, puppies under 4 months of age should be kept out of public parks and other public areas.

Constipation

PUPPIES
Possible Signs

- 🐾 straining or frequent attempts to have a bowel movement (sometimes resulting in a small amount of liquid stool that looks like diarrhea)
- 🐾 pain while passing stools (whimpering)
- 🐾 hard, pebble-like stools
- 🐾 may be blood on the surface of the stool
- 🐾 fewer bowel movements than usual (a reduced number of "messes" in the house)
- 🐾 hunched appearance (abdominal discomfort, or "bellyache")

Summary

We need to remember that each puppy is an individual; therefore the number of bowel movements produced in a day will vary with each puppy. We must also remember that on average puppies have a larger number of bowel movements per day than adult dogs. Knowing your puppy's regular routine is the best way of being able to spot a problem. Watch for signs like trouble passing stool (usually dry and hard) or fewer "messes" in the house. Constipation in puppies can often be caused by frequent changes in the brand of food they are being fed or by pieces of things that your puppy has swallowed as it has chewed its way through the house. If treated early, constipation can be easily overcome. If left for a period of time, however, it can lead to secondary signs of illness such as vomiting and lethargy.

Do not cut back on a puppy's fluid intake to keep it from urinating in the house. Puppies need water to survive!

Constipation

Puppies

Is your pup obviously in pain when trying to pass stool?

or

Is your pup showing signs of secondary illness (vomiting, loss of appetite)?

 YES **CALL YOUR VET**

 NO

Has your pup produced any stool within the last 24 hours?

NO → If there is a physical obstruction around the rectum (e.g., mat of hair, hard poop), use **HOME SUGGESTIONS**.

If no improvement, or no obstruction,

CALL YOUR VET

 YES

Is there blood or foreign material visible in the stool?

 YES **CALL YOUR VET**

 NO

Have you changed your pup's diet (brand change, human food, decreased fluid)?

or

Has your pup been into anything (bones, cat litter, garbage, pieces of toys, etc.)?

or

Have you changed your pup's environment or regular routine (less activity, more time in the kennel, etc.)?

If your pup appears depressed or in distress at any time during treatment, or if the constipation persists, CALL YOUR VET.

 YES

use **HOME SUGGESTIONS**

Is the problem persisting beyond 24 to 48 hours?

YES **CALL YOUR VET**

Home Suggestions

1. The first thing to do, if you can get your puppy to stay still long enough, is to look under its tail. Hair and poop often collect into a mat around the rectum, causing a physical barrier. A rule of thumb: If you cannot see where the stool comes out, chances are it *can't* come out. Warm-water rinses or cloths can be used first to loosen the mat. It may be necessary to gently clip the hair away from the skin, but make sure you "look before you snip." You do not want more than just the hair coming off.

2. Very young puppies are unable to produce bowel movements on their own until they are about 4 weeks of age. They normally require stimulation around the rectum by their mother's tongue during regular grooming. This same action can be done for orphaned puppies or for those that are having some difficulty with bowel movements. Don't be grossed out yet; you can substitute a warm, moist cotton ball for a tongue. Perform gentle movements with the cotton ball around the rectum for several minutes.

3. Puppies are generally very active creatures requiring a lot of daily exercise. This activity is not only important for tiring the puppy out so that we can keep our sanity by the end of the day; it is also necessary to ensure regular bowel movements by the puppy. Taking it on a leash walk 20 minutes after eating is very helpful. In deep-chested dogs, activity after eating can lead to bloat.

4. Fluids are an important part of preventing and treating constipation. If your puppy is not interested in drinking just water, try adding a splash of milk, tuna juice or even **Gatorade**. Frozen ice cubes can also be used as treats. The puppy will never know they are made of water.

5. Laxatives should be used more cautiously in puppies (see **Constipation in Adult Dogs**, page 44). A mixture of 50:50 corn syrup and water given orally will work just as well for these little guys.

6. Fiber is an important factor in keeping your puppy regular. If for some reason, the puppy's regular diet is not doing the trick, try some of these products that are found at home:
   - Psyllium fiber (**Metamucil** and others) (1 to 5 tsp or 5 to 25 mL daily with food)
   - Canned pumpkin (1 to 5 tbsp or 15 to 75 mL daily with food)

7. Ask yourself these questions:

- Has the puppy been let outside often enough?
- Have there been any disruptive changes to the puppy's regular routine?
- Has the puppy been getting enough activity lately?
- Is the puppy on any medication that could be causing constipation?
- What is the puppy eating other than its own food (bones, toys, garbage, human food, cat litter)? (Has one of Teddy's eyes stared up at you from a pile of the puppy's poop yet?)
- Do you keep changing the brand of puppy food that you buy?

> *Enemas are not recommended as a home treatment; you may cause further damage, and it is better to let the vet have all the fun.*

Coughing

PUPPIES
Possible Signs

- forceful movement of air out of the mouth
- audible sounds (hacking/honking)
- production of phlegm (gagging, swallowing at end of cough)
- secondary signs—minor: sneezing and reverse sneezing
                    serious: fatigue, shortness of breath, collapse,
                    purple color to gums

Summary

Puppies are very curious and will often butt their way into anything, often nose first. Whether the puppy has been chewing on sticks or digging in the dirt, a throat irritation leading to a cough is often unavoidable. There are numerous things that can cause a cough, ranging from environmental irritants (dust, pollen and smoke), to more serious health concerns—such as birth defects that can lead a dog to breathe in particles of food. Viruses, parasites, bacteria and even abnormalities of the airways are also possible culprits. It is important to try to determine the underlying cause. Always try to find out if the puppy has been in contact with other dogs (at kennels or grooming centers) and if the other dogs have been coughing (e.g., kennel cough). A cough can be annoying, but it is a natural reflex that often helps to get rid of something that is not supposed to be in either the lungs or in the windpipe.

Coughing

Puppies

Is your pup experiencing any shortness of breath or trouble breathing? — **YES**

Check for foreign body in mouth. If present, remove. If unable to remove, **CALL YOUR VET**

 NO

Is your pup showing any signs of generalized illness (listlessness, poor eating, etc.)? — **YES** — **CALL YOUR VET**

 NO

Is the cough "productive" (wet or moist—phlegm may be seen or puppy may swallow after each cough)?

or

Do you notice any blood? (Check for access to mouse/rat poison; if possible, take the container to veterinarian.) — **YES** — **CALL YOUR VET**

 NO

Does your pup have any other conditions? (Have you noticed milk or food coming out of its nose when your pup is eating? Does it bring up small amounts of food following eating?) — **YES** — **CALL YOUR VET**

 NO

use HOME SUGGESTIONS

Is the cough persisting beyond 2 to 3 days, or is your pup in distress? — **YES** — **CALL YOUR VET**

Home Suggestions

1. Try to reduce environmental irritants, such as smoke, dust, perfume, etc., that can irritate the throat. (This can be tough—a puppy can stir up dust even Martha Stewart would not have seen in the house.)

2. Try increasing the humidity in your home by using a humidifier or even a vaporizer like mom used to use when you had a cough as a kid. Increased humidity in your house can make it easier for your pup to breathe.

3. Sometimes using a chest or face harness instead of a collar will help by putting less pressure on the puppy's windpipe when he is pulling (we know obedience classes don't start for a while yet). This approach works especially well with small-breed dogs. Avoid using choke chains.

4. Avoid heat and stressful situations. Although it can be difficult, also try to restrict your puppy's activity until the cough goes away or is treated.

5. Reduce the amount of chewing that your puppy does (easier said than done); sometimes small particles of debris (e.g., sticks) caught in the throat can produce quite a cough. Rubber or stuffed toys that are indestructible are fine for your pup to chew on.

6. Avoid using any medication on puppies unless absolutely necessary. See **Coughing in Adult Dogs,** page 48.

7. Raise your puppy's dishes off the ground or use softened food, if the puppy's coughing is more frequent during feeding time. Some pups literally "inhale" their food. Raising your puppy's dishes off the ground or using softened food may help reduce the amount of coughing by slowing the rate at which the puppy eats.

8. Keep your puppy away from other dogs, just in case it is infectious.

9. Some pups "inhale" food. To slow the puppy down, place a large toy in the bowl so that the pup has to eat around it.

Ear Infections

PUPPIES
Possible Signs

- excessive scratching of ears
- head shaking
- smelly ears
- discharge from ears
- mild depression, not playful
- resists petting of the head or may encourage scratching of ears

Summary

Ear infections in puppies are very common. Most ear infections in puppies are located in the ear canal and very rarely in the middle ear. Parasites (ear mites are common in puppies), bacteria and yeast are the most common types of ear infections. When you look down a puppy's ears, you must actually pull the ear open slightly. Look for dirt and debris deep down in the ear. Superficial dirt on the earflap (*pinnae*) can be the result of playing and digging and is not important.

Smell the ears. Yeast infections do not always produce a lot of debris but they do smell funny.

Pups that possess a lot of hair in their ears (poodles, shih tzus) can be more difficult to examine. Gently tease the hair outward from the ear canal so that your vision is not impaired.

Pups that are water dogs (golden retrievers, Labrador retrievers) have more ear infections and must be monitored constantly.

Most ear infections require a veterinarian's intervention for treatment. However, you can obtain short-term relief for your puppy by gently cleaning its ears. Cotton balls are best for cleaning; *never use **Q-tips** in a dog's ears.*

Ear Infections

Puppies

**Does your pup have: A painful ear?
Discharge from the ear? A smelly ear?**

or

Do you suspect an ear infection?

 YES

**Examine the affected ear. Look down the ear canal
(see section on physical exams, pages 4 to 6,
and be careful!).**

Do you see dirt and debris, or is the pup clearly in pain?   YES

> Use **TREATMENT A** from
> **HOME SUGGESTIONS**. If pup
> improves, continue treatment.
>
> If no improvement,
>
> **CALL YOUR VET**

 NO

Is there the appearance of coffee grounds in the ear?   YES

> Use **TREATMENT B** from
> **HOME SUGGESTIONS**, and
>
> **CALL YOUR VET**

 NO

**Is the ear mildly dirty, but your pup doesn't
appear to be in pain?**   YES

> Use **TREATMENT A**
> from **HOME SUGGESTIONS**.
> If the ear returns to normal,
> monitor closely.

> If signs are very mild, repeat
> **TREATMENT A.**
>
> If symptoms persist or return,
>
> **CALL YOUR VET**

Home Suggestions

It is important to note that most ear infections will require the assistance of a veterinarian.

1. Obtain instructions for proper ear care from your veterinarian for your breed of puppy. Puppies that are prone to ear infections should be examined by the owner weekly (use treats and make it a good experience for the pup).

2. **Treatment A:** Temporary relief for your puppy can be obtained by introducing a warm solution of water and white vinegar (50:50) into the ear using a syringe. The pup must be prevented from shaking out the solution for a period of 1 minute. Gentle swabbing of the ear canal with cotton balls will remove debris.

   - Commercial preparations of ear cleaners are widely available and are balanced, slightly acidic solutions. These are not expensive and are recommended for your pup's medicine chest, especially for owners of water-loving pups.

   - Overuse of ear cleaners can irritate your pup's ear. A rule of thumb is that if there is no improvement after two cleanings, see the veterinarian.

   Treatment B: If ear mites are suspected (they look like coffee grounds in the ear), mineral oil or baby oil may bring temporary relief. See your vet ASAP, but please not in the middle of the night.

3. Pups with large amounts of hair in the ear canal require either gentle teasing (or grooming) of the hair to grow out of the ear canal or plucking of the hair out of the ear.

   - It is our opinion that, if the owner or groomer would like to "pluck" the hair from the pup's ear, he/she should do this on a regular basis (every 4 weeks). However, plucking the hair from a dirty ear or a mildly infected ear will make the condition worse.

   Authors' note: We are teasers, not "pluckers."

Eye Problems

PUPPIES
Possible Signs

- more than normal or greenish discharge from one or both eyes
- redness or cloudiness
- squinting or sensitivity to light
- rubbing of the eyes (pain)
- swelling of area around eyes
- excessive tearing

Problem Animals

- Pups with pushed-in noses. These pups have folds of skin beneath their eyes, and the hair covering these folds can touch the eye itself (e.g., bulldogs, shih tzus)
- Pups with hairs (called *cilia*) on their eyelids that fold in and touch the eye (e.g., poodles)
- Pups with eyelids that either roll into the eye (e.g., shar-pei) and cause irritation or droop (e.g., bloodhounds) and don't cover the eye

Summary

Eye problems are common in puppies. They range greatly in severity from the mildest case of excessive tearing, to an acute injury or serious infection. Due to the extreme differences in breeds, it is very important that you ask the vet on the first puppy visit to point out the areas around your pup's eyes that could be a potential problem.

Flushing the eye and the skin around the eye with warm water is the simplest and most effective form of eye care and emergency treatment. It is important never to ignore eye problems; an examination by your veterinarian and early treatment can save the eyesight of your pet.

Eye Problems

Puppies

Has your pup been in an accident involving the eye? **YES**  **CALL YOUR VET**

 NO

Is your pup a "problem breed" (see page 27)? **YES** **CALL YOUR VET**
Ask for suggestions on routine eye care for your breed of puppy

 NO

Is one eye cloudy or larger than the other? **YES** **CALL YOUR VET**

 NO

Is the area around the eye slowly swelling?
and/or
Does your pup have a history of bug bites? **YES** See **BUG BITES AND REACTIONS**, page 65, then return to this page.
and/or
Does your pup have a history of allergies?

 NO

Is the eye severely painful or irritated? **YES** Flush eye with water or contact lens solution and **CALL YOUR VET**

 NO

Is the eye mildly painful or irritated?

 YES

Flush eye with water or contact lens solution, and monitor closely.

 *Do not ignore eye problems; a chronic eye problem can result in severe damage to the eye. If you have any concerns, **CALL YOUR VET**.*

Home Suggestions

1. Regular examinations of your pup's eyes will allow you to quickly identify problem areas. It is important to know what "normal" looks like.

2. Have your vet point out any areas that can potentially cause problems with your pup's eyes or the area around the eyes.

   - Pups with flattened noses can have an excess amount of skin beneath the eyes. Hairs from the folds can touch the eyes, causing excessive tearing that produces a "gunk" at the corners of the eyes.

     Clean these skin folds with warm water daily. This removes the gunk that builds up. (Make this daily care a good experience for your pet by giving the pup a treat after every wash.)

   - Other causes of eye gunk are problem eyelashes or problem eyelids. The treatment consists of daily washing with warm water. Sometimes corrective surgery is required.

3. Pups that are rubbing their eyes or squinting require an immediate examination of the eye. If you cannot identify and correct the problem, see your vet. Pups will cause more damage if they accidentally scratch their cornea.

   - Allergic reactions can sometimes cause swelling around the eyes or cause eye problems (redness and inflammation) directly. See the section on allergic reaction (page 65) for treatment.

4. An eye injury can be very serious. Examine the eye and flush with large amounts of water or contact lens solution. Flushing can either remove a foreign body from the eye or it can dilute an irritating chemical like a shampoo. See your vet immediately if the condition does not resolve with flushing the eye.

Skin Problems

PUPPIES
Possible Signs

- red or inflamed areas
- hair loss/change in skin color
- increased dandruff and shedding
- itchiness (scratching)
- open sores
- parasites visible (fleas, ticks, walking dandruff mites)

Summary

Like adult dogs, puppies are able to develop a variety of skin conditions that can be classified as bacterial/fungal/hormonal/parasitic/allergic and abnormal immune responses. However, more commonly, the puppy's skin is just reacting to things in its environment, such as a poor-quality diet, intestinal worms or overbathing. Some skin conditions can easily be prevented by following a few simple suggestions, while others may require veterinary assistance.

Skin Problems

Puppies

Is your pup showing other signs of illness?

or

Is your pup "scratching itself silly"?

YES  **CALL YOUR VET**

 NO

Is there evidence of fleas, ticks, etc.?

YES → See **ATTACK OF THE CRITTERS**, page 79, then return to this page.

 NO

Don't stop looking for critters; this is the number one cause of skin problems in puppies.

Are there small raw patches on your pup's skin?

YES → Try **HOT SPOT SUGGESTIONS**, page 33, then return to this page.

 NO

Is there evidence of blisters, ulcers or pus?

or

Are there large raw areas on your pup's skin?

YES **CALL YOUR VET**

 NO

Are there areas of hair loss (balding) on your pup's coat?

or

Is there darkening of the skin?

or

Is your pup's coat dry?

YES *use* **HOME SUGGESTIONS**

If improvement is not noticed in 4 to 5 days,

CALL YOUR VET

 A skin problem can be extremely frustrating for the owner and for the veterinarian. Proper grooming practices and attention to "critter control" solve many puppy skin conditions.

Home Suggestions

1. Proper grooming plays a very important role in helping to maintain a healthy haircoat and skin. It is important to start a regular routine early on in life so that the puppy gets used to being handled. Often the longer you wait to start a grooming program, the more difficult it can be. For information about proper grooming for different breeds, see **Skin Problems in Adult Dogs**, page 57.

2. It is very important that the skin stays nice and dry in order to prevent bacterial infections from starting:

   - make sure that your puppy gets dried off after bathing or swimming, using either a towel or a hair dryer (start out slowly at a low heat as this can be scary for some puppies).

   - Keep the collar off until your puppy is dry to prevent moisture from being trapped against the skin.

   - Keep higher-moisture areas clean and dry—between the toes, around the eyes and along the lips.

3. Contrary to popular belief, licking does not promote healing of sores. (If only it were that simple.) In some instances, puppies will actually cause self-mutilation. In order to prevent licking, you can try some different ideas:

   - Use a piece of clothing to cover the sore, for example a T-shirt or baby clothes (Beware: Puppies don't always appreciate being dressed up and have been known to shred clothing.)

   - Create an at-home version of the "Elizabethan collar" using an ice cream pail or plastic bottle. Cut an area large enough for the puppy's head to fit through snugly, but not big enough so that the puppy can easily slip its head out. Make sure you tape the cut edges of the pail to prevent irritation to the pup's neck. (Some advice: clear all the valuable china off the tables before putting on the collar.)

   - Try a nasty-tasting spray that goes around the wound (e.g., **Bitter Apple**).

   Tabasco sauce is **not** recommended. Using it may lead you to turn to the section on diarrhea (just a helpful hint).

4. Although puppies seem to get dirty every time they are outside, they should not be bathed each time. Shampooing strips the natural oils from the haircoat, causing dandruff and itchiness. Rinsing the dirty areas with water will often do the trick. Use a dog shampoo. A bath every 6 weeks is plenty unless medicated baths are required and indicated by your vet. Use a dog shampoo and a dog conditioner.

5. Make sure that your puppy is on a good quality food. Not all brands are the same, and generally the lower the price tag the lower the quality of food. Low-quality puppy foods tend to lack the essential fatty acids that the haircoat needs to remain healthy. Deworming puppies will often make a huge difference in the haircoat and general health.

6. Remember that dogs will get drier in the winter because of the drop in air humidity. Using a humidifier in your home will benefit both your puppy and your family. Your vet can supply you with a spray moisturizer for serious cases of dry skin.

7. Allergies can cause a real problem, especially in the spring and summer months, although puppies will usually not develop signs until they are a little older. Trying to avoid the cause of the reaction is best, but difficult in most cases. An antihistamine should be used with caution in young puppies. For more information, see **Skin Problems of Adult Dogs**, page 57.

8. Parasite control (see **Attack of the Critters**, page 79).

9. In the summer, "hot spots" or localized areas of infection occur frequently. The first step is to clip the hair close to the skin. Keep the area nice and clean using a diluted peroxide solution, and make sure that the sore is kept dry.

Loss of Appetite

ADULT DOGS
Possible Signs

- refusal to eat (may still drink)
- possible swollen abdomen (potbelly)
- may vomit
- lethargy (tired and depressed)

Summary

Most dogs will stop eating for a day or so due to dietary indiscretion (he ate something he wasn't supposed to, or "garbage guts") and there is nothing to worry about. A proper history of the dog's eating habits and problem chewing behavior will give clues as to the cause of the lack of appetite. If the dog remains bright and alert, but not hungry, there is usually less to be concerned about.

Loss of appetite combined with other clinical signs such as vomiting or diarrhea tend to be more serious.

Attempting to slowly introduce the dog back to food with a soothing diet is an important treatment method.

Loss of Appetite

ADULT DOGS

Has your dog been "eating out" (ask all family members and neighbors)? — **YES** → Set some rules for feeding the dog.

NO

Is yours a non-neutered dog in breeding season? — **YES** → Consider all other causes and monitor closely.

NO

Does your dog appear to have a painful mouth when chewing? — **YES** → See **DENTAL DISEASE**, page 69, then return to this page.

NO

Is your dog constipated (not pooping)? — **YES** → See **CONSTIPATION IN ADULT DOGS**, page 44, then return to this page.

NO

Is your dog vomiting? — **YES** → See **VOMITING IN ADULT DOGS** page 37, then return to this page.

NO

Is your dog drinking water? — **NO** → **CALL YOUR VET**

YES

Will your dog eat small amounts of appetizing food (see **HOME SUGGESTIONS**)? — **NO** → **CALL YOUR VET**

YES

Tempt your dog with other types or brands of food. Be careful—dogs can wait for days to have home cooking! Given the chance, dogs will train the owners to give them only the very best.

Adult dogs that are not eating may have a serious underlying illness (e.g., cancer). If you have concerns, CALL YOUR VET.

Home Suggestions

1. Tempt your dog with **small amounts** (a tablespoon or two) of appetizing food (chicken, hamburger mixed with rice or boiled potatoes). Also, try ketchup or garlic powder to enhance the flavor of the food. If the dog will eat this food, slowly increase the amount. Start to blend in the regular diet with this over a day or two.

2. Observe and record any vomiting or bowel movements. Look for bits of blood, plastic, cloth—basically everything but the kitchen sink. This is very useful information for your veterinarian and will guide the vet towards the correct diagnostic tests (x rays, blood work, fecal exams, etc.).

3. Record the length of time since the dog has last eaten. Ask all family members and neighbors if the dog has been fed by someone. (Dogs are the best beggars in the world, and those eyes can melt even the coldest heart.) Many cases of loss of appetite can be traced to the dog finding an alternative source of food. In these cases, the dogs are typically still playful and active.

4. Non-neutered dogs can go off food during breeding periods. (Who wants to think about food, right?)

5. Periods of prolonged loss of appetite require a veterinarian's attention. Cancer and other major diseases can result in chronic loss of appetite or chronic weight loss. If your dog is losing weight, listless or depressed, have it checked by your vet.

Vomiting

ADULT DOGS
Possible Signs

- vomiting (throwing up)

And some or all of the following:

- loss of appetite (not eating)
- diarrhea (loose poop) or constipation (not pooping)
- swollen abdomen (potbelly)
- painful abdomen
- drooling

Summary

Dogs have a built-in safety device; they can throw up on command. Considering that most dogs are known to forage for some pretty unsavory items and eat them, this ability is a good thing (for them, not us).

All dogs vomit occasionally and, for the most part, treatment is minimal, consisting of the removal of additional food and monitoring the dog. Occasionally, food must be removed for a day, followed by a slow re-introduction to food using a soothing diet (see recipe), page 39.

Serious cases of vomiting require the assistance of your veterinarian. This includes cases of prolonged, repeated vomiting, projectile vomiting, bloated or painful abdomen and the presence of digested blood in the vomit (it is black and looks like coffee grounds).

The degree of danger associated with repeated vomiting varies with the size and age of your dog. The smaller and/or younger the dog, the more quickly you should seek help. If your dog is depressed or obviously in distress, take it to the vet. If the dog remains bright and alert after vomiting, simply keep a close watch for signs of distress.

If in doubt, call your vet.

Vomiting

ADULT DOGS

Is your dog vomiting blood or digested blood (black and looks like coffee grounds)?

or

Is your dog bloated (very large belly)?

or

Has your dog had bouts of prolonged repeated vomiting?

YES →  **CALL YOUR VET**

 NO

Is it possible that there is poison in the vomit (mouse, slug bait, etc.; the vomit might be blue or green)?

YES → **CALL YOUR VET**

 NO

Are there foreign bodies in the vomit (bones, sticks, kitchen sinks, etc.)?

YES → **CALL YOUR VET**

 NO

Does your dog feel better after vomiting?

NO → **CALL YOUR VET**

 YES

use HOME SUGGESTIONS

Is there prolonged vomiting?

YES →  **CALL YOUR VET**

 NO

Monitor for additional vomiting.

Home Suggestions

1. Before cleaning up the vomit, examine it and try to determine the cause of the vomiting (use something such as a stick to stir it up). Look for: plastic, bone fragments, pieces of wood, cloth and just about anything else you can think of.

2. Ask yourself and family members the following questions:
   - Did you change the brand of dog food or buy a new bag of food?
   - Did you give the dog some treats or bones recently?
   - Has your dog been outside or visiting neighbors without your supervision?
   - Has your dog just eaten a very large amount of food?

   The above questions and your own observations will typically reveal the cause of the vomiting and you can act accordingly.

3. **Simple treatment:** Use this treatment when the dog appears normal and you believe the cause to be dietary indiscretion ("garbage guts" as we say in the trade). In most cases the dog recovers quickly after vomiting.
   - Withhold food and allow the digestive tract time to recover, generally 24 hours.
   - Try to give the dog very small amounts of water and monitor for additional vomiting.
   - Use a soothing diet of :
     - Cooked hamburger and cooked rice (50:50); or
     - Cooked hamburger and boiled potatoes (50:50)
   - Feed very small amounts of food to the dog, frequently
     - For example: 1 tbsp (15 mL) every hour
   - As the dog recovers, increase the amount of food and decrease the frequency
     - For example: 3 tbsp (45 mL) every 2 hours
     - Adjust volumes and frequency accordingly for the size of your dog
   - As the dog recovers, start mixing in your usual dog food with the soothing diet. (Some dogs resist the return to the old dog food because the soothing diet is "just so darn good." Be firm or you will be cooking for your dog forever.)

4. It is common to notice diarrhea following a bout of vomiting. Examining the stool will sometimes reveal the initial cause of your dog's problems—socks, toys, bones, shoes, strings, rocks, lingerie, etc. (I once treated a dog that ate so much sand that when it passed, it looked like a beach.) Diarrhea that contains blood (blood can appear bright red, black and tarry, or like strawberry jam) should be investigated by your veterinarian. Some cases of viral diarrhea and vomiting are life threatening; **DO NOT** "wait and see."

5. Evidence of serious cases of vomiting:

- Prolonged, repeated vomiting (longer than 24 hours or continual vomiting)
- Swollen abdomen (usually on the left side of the dog; look at the dog from a few feet away and watch for asymmetry)
- Digested blood (black and looks like coffee grounds)

For all serious cases or suspected serious cases of vomiting, **CALL YOUR VET** immediately.

Diarrhea

ADULT DOGS
Possible Signs

- watery or loose bowel movements
- straining
- increased frequency of bowel movements (accidents or "messes" in house)
- may see secondary changes: blood in stool or black stools; reduced appetite; depression; vomiting

Summary

Most dogs will eat just about anything if given the chance. It is for these reasons that most dog owners will have experienced a bout of doggy diarrhea at one time or another. Dietary indiscretion cases ("garbage guts") seem to be some of the most common; however, there are many other potential causes of diarrhea, including infectious agents like viruses and bacteria, intestinal parasites and even certain medications. Most cases of diarrhea will resolve on their own within several days if we are patient. In some cases, however, it can be very serious. One very important thing to remember is that dogs with diarrhea are losing a lot of fluid from their body, and can become dehydrated quickly, therefore extra care must be taken to make sure that dehydration does not develop.

Diarrhea

ADULT DOGS

Has the diarrhea been present for 3 to 4 days?

or

Is your dog depressed or lethargic?

or

Are there signs of abdominal pain
(hunched or whining) or bloating?

YES **CALL YOUR VET**

 NO

Is your dog vomiting?

YES — See **VOMITING IN ADULT DOGS,** page 37, then return to this page.

 NO

Has your dog been dewormed or checked
for intestinal parasites?

NO **CALL YOUR VET**

 YES

Is there blood in the diarrhea?

YES **CALL YOUR VET**

 NO

Have you changed your dog's diet recently?

or

Has your dog eaten something it shouldn't
have (furniture, dirty laundry, sticks and
stones, bones, etc.)?

or

Is your dog getting a lot of human food?

 YES

use HOME SUGGESTIONS

Monitor your dog closely for changes.

 Diarrhea is extremely common in dogs, especially young dogs. Monitor closely, and if concerned, CALL YOUR VET.

Home Suggestions

1. Ensure that your dog has access to plenty of water, since diarrhea can often lead to dehydration. Some people also like to use electrolyte solutions, such as **Pedialyte** and **Gatorade**. Leave a dish of water down at all times.

2. Fasting the dog for a 24-hour period will give the animal's system a bit of a break; this includes treats as well as food.

3. Next, gradually re-introduce small amounts of a very soothing diet. Some suggestions include rice, potatoes, macaroni and lean chicken. Avoid foods high in fat or lactose (milk, cheese). As stools start to firm up, mix in your dog's regular diet in increasing amounts for another 4 to 5 days.

4. Medications can be used to alter the frequency of diarrhea, but will not actually be able to cure the problem. Most cases of diarrhea will run their course within 3 to 4 days. If however, you need to take the dog from the cottage to home without an unpleasant accident in the car you can try some of the following:

   - **Pepto-Bismol** (*bismuth subsalicylate*) (1/4 to 3/4 tsp or 1 to 3 mL per kg divided over the day)
     Produces a dark, tarry stool that quickly stains carpets and is often mistaken for digested blood
     Difficult to administer without the dog looking like it is wearing pink lipstick
     (Available in a tablet form also)
   - **Kaopectate** (1/4 to 1/2 tsp or 1 to 2 mL per kg every 2 to 4 hours)
   - Loperamide (**Imodium** and others) (0.1 to 0.2 mg per kg every 12 hours)
     Caution: overuse can produce a rebound effect, leading to constipation and stomach pain.

5. Questions to ask yourself:
   - Has your dog been dewormed or checked for intestinal parasites?
   - Has your dog had its appropriate vaccinations?
   - Has your dog eaten anything it is not supposed to? (bones, garbage, toys)
   - Have you recently changed the brand of dog food?
   - Is your dog on any form of medication?

Constipation

ADULT DOGS
Possible Signs

- straining or frequent attempts to have a bowel movement (sometimes resulting in a small amount of liquid stool that looks like diarrhea)
- pain while passing stools (whimpering)
- hard, dry stools
- infrequent bowel movements
- hunched appearance (abdominal discomfort or "bellyache")

Summary

Each dog is an individual, therefore the number of bowel movements produced in a day will vary. Some will only go once a day while others may go as frequently as 4 or 5 times. A dog's diet is often the major factor that controls the amount normally produced. To spot a problem, look for any change in your dog's regular routine, including any difficulty in passing stool (usually dry and hard), to a decrease in the number of bowel movements in a day. Constipation will tend to vary with a dog's age, activity level and type of diet, as well as the amount of fluids the dog consumes. If treated early, constipation can be easily overcome. If left for a period of time, however, it can lead to secondary signs of illness such as vomiting, loss of appetite, and depression.

Note: Older dogs (especially female ones) may lose bladder control as they age. Your vet can prescribe something to help this. **Do not** cut back on the dog's fluid intake. Dogs need water to survive.

Constipation

ADULT DOGS

Is this a recurring problem?

or

Is your dog obviously in pain while trying to pass stool?

or

Is your dog showing signs of secondary illness
(vomiting, loss of appetite)?

 NO

Has your dog produced any stool within the last 24 hours?

 YES

Is there blood or foeign material visible in the stool?

 NO

Have you changed your dog's diet (brand change,
human food, decreased fluid)?

or

Has your dog been into anything (bones, cat litter,
garbage, pieces of toys, etc.)?

or

Have you changed your dog's environment or regular
routine (less activity, more time in the kennel, etc.)?

 YES

use HOME SUGGESTIONS

Is the problem persisting beyond 24 hours?

YES — **CALL YOUR VET**

YES — **CALL YOUR VET**

NO — If there is a physical
obstruction around the rectum
(e.g., mat of hair, hard poop),
use **HOME SUGGESTIONS**.

If no improvement,

CALL YOUR VET

YES — **CALL YOUR VET**

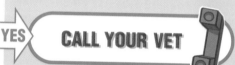

If your dog appears
depressed or in distress at
any time during treatment,
or if the constipation persists,
CALL YOUR VET.

Home Suggestions

1. The first thing to do is to "hike up" your dog's tail and have a good look. Can you see the rectum? If not, then there is a good chance that stool will not be able to pass. Hair and poop often collect into a mat around the rectum, causing a physical barrier. Often a soak in warm water or warm wet cloths will loosen any material caught in the hair. In some cases the mat may have to be removed by gently clipping the hair away. Before going ahead blindly, make sure that you can see all the important parts of the dog (a female's vulva and a male's scrotum). If any skin is clipped accidentally, turn to **Bleeding Wounds**, page 63.

2. It is important to make sure your dog is getting enough activity to help stimulate a bowel movement. A lazy dog often results in a lazy bowel (point of optimism—carry a poop pick-up bag with you).

3. Fluids are an important part of preventing and treating constipation. If your dog is not interested in drinking much water, try adding a splash of tuna juice or some milk for flavor. For those that aren't fooled by that trick, try ice cubes as treats.

4. An increase in the amount of fiber in the diet can help with your dog's regularity. Older dogs are like older people and they sometimes need help in this area. Some commercially available diets are specific to this condition, but some home sources of fiber include:
    - Natural bran (1 to 5 tbsp or 15 to 75 mL daily with food)
    - Psyllium fiber (**Metamucil** and others) (1 to 5 tsp or 5 to 25 mL daily with food)
    - Canned pumpkin (1 to 5 tbsp or 15 to 75 mL daily with food)

5. Laxatives can also be used to loosen things up.
    - Mineral oil—give with a few drops of vanilla flavoring (1 to 5 tsp or 5 to 25 mL daily)
    - **Laxatone** or other petroleum-based hairball remedies (1/4 to 1 tsp or 1.25 to 5 mL daily)

Ex-lax is not recommended for use in dogs. Laxatives should not be used if the dog is vomiting. Enemas should not be attempted at home.

6. Ask yourself these questions:

- 🐾 Has the dog been let outside often enough?
- 🐾 Have there been any disruptive changes to the dog's regular routine?
- 🐾 Has the dog been getting enough activity lately?
- 🐾 Is the dog on any medication that could be causing constipation?
- 🐾 Has the dog been having other hind-end problems that may cause it to have difficulty going to the bathroom (anal gland problems, hind-end stiffness)?
- 🐾 What is the dog eating other than its own food (bones, toys, garbage, human food, etc.)?
- 🐾 Do you keep changing the brand of dog food you buy?

Coughing

ADULT DOGS
Possible Signs

- forceful movement of air out of the mouth
- audible sounds (hacking/honking)
- production of phlegm (gagging, swallowing at end of cough)
- secondary signs—minor: sneezing and reverse sneezing

    serious: fatigue, shortness of breath, collapse,

    purple color to gums

Summary

Dogs cough as a natural reflex in response to airway irritation. There are numerous things that can cause a cough, ranging from environmental irritants (dust, pollen and smoke), to more serious health concerns like congestive heart failure. Viruses, parasites, bacterial agents and even abnormalities of the airways are also possible culprits. It is important to try to determine the underlying cause. (Pay special attention if your dog has been boarded recently or been to a grooming parlour.) In some cases the cough is nothing but annoying, but in others it is a natural defense mechanism to prevent the body from literally drowning in its own fluids.

Coughing

ADULT DOGS

Is the dog experiencing any shortness of breath or trouble breathing?

or

Is it a recurring problem?

YES → **CALL YOUR VET**

 NO

Is the dog showing any signs of generalized illness (listlessness, poor eating, etc.)?

YES → **CALL YOUR VET**

 NO

Is the cough "productive" (wet or moist—phlegm may be seen or your dog may swallow after each cough)?

or

Do you notice any blood?

YES → **CALL YOUR VET**

 NO

Does the dog have any other conditions?

or

Is the dog on any type of medication?

YES → **CALL YOUR VET**

 NO

use HOME SUGGESTIONS

Is the cough persisting after 4 to 5 days, or is your dog in distress?

YES → **CALL YOUR VET**

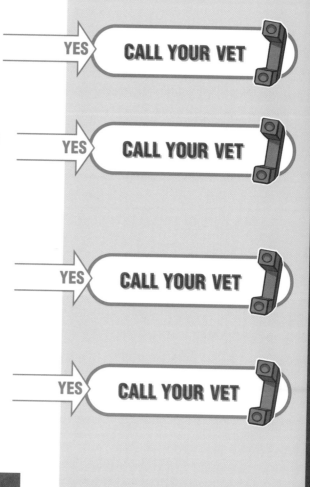

Home Suggestions

1. Try to reduce environmental irritants such as smoke, dust, perfume (not always easy for some of us), etc., that can irritate the throat.

2. Using a humidifier or vaporizer in your house can often make it easier for a dog with a cough to breathe. (Don't you remember mom doing that for you as a child? However, **Vicks** is not necessary.)

3. Try using a harness instead of a collar, therefore putting less pressure on the dog's windpipe. This approach works well with small-breed dogs who are more prone to windpipe problems like "collapsing tracheas."

4. Avoid heat and stressful situations. Also try to restrict your dog's activity until the cough goes away or is treated.

5. Reduce the amount of chewing that your dog does. Sometimes, small particles of debris caught in the throat can produce quite a cough (e.g., sticks).

6. Medication should be used cautiously with coughing dogs. A dry hacking cough will often be calmed by a cough suppressant such as dextromethorphan. Remember two things:
    - Make sure the cough suppressant is not mixed with other medications
    - Do not use the cough suppressant if the cough is "productive" (wet or moist cough)

Ear Infections

ADULT DOGS
Possible Signs

- ❧ excessive scratching of ears
- ❧ smelly ears
- ❧ discharge from ears
- ❧ mild depression, not playful
- ❧ resists petting of the head or may encourage scratching of ears

Summary

Ear infections in dogs are very common. Most ear infections in dogs are located in the ear canal and very rarely in the middle ear or inner ear. Parasites (ear mites are more common in puppies), bacteria and yeast are the most common types of ear infections. While examining a dog's ears, be careful: an infected ear can be painful. Look for dirt and debris deep down in the ear. Smell the ears; yeast infections do not always produce a noticeable discharge but they do smell funny and it ain't bread that is cooking!

Dogs that possess long hair in their ear canal (poodles, shih tzus) can be difficult to examine. Gently tease the hair outward from the ear canal so that your vision is not impaired. Water dogs (Labrador retrievers, Springer spaniels) and dogs with big floppy ears (basset hounds, cocker spaniels) have more ear infections and must be monitored constantly.

Prevention is the key to healthy ears. A discussion of ear care for your particular breed of dog with your veterinarian is essential. If your dog has an ear infection, see your vet.

Ear Infections

ADULT DOGS

**Does your dog have: A painful ear?
Discharge from the ear? A smelly ear?**

 YES

**Examine the affected ear. Look down the ear canal
(see sections on physical exams, and be careful!).**

Do you see dirt and debris, or is your dog clearly in pain?   YES →

Use **TREATMENT A** from **HOME
SUGGESTIONS**. If dog improves,
continue treatment.

If no improvement,

CALL YOUR VET

 NO

Is there the appearance of coffee grounds in the ear?   YES →

Use **TREATMENT B** from **HOME
SUGGESTIONS**. If dog improves,
continue treatment.

If no improvement,

CALL YOUR VET

 NO

**Is the ear mildly dirty, but your dog doesn't
appear to be in pain?**   YES →

Use **TREATMENT A**
from **HOME SUGGESTIONS**.
If the ear returns to normal,
monitor closely.

If signs are very mild, repeat
TREATMENT A.

If symptoms persist or return,

CALL YOUR VET

Home Suggestions

It is important to note that most ear infections will require the assistance of a veterinarian.

1. Obtain instructions for proper ear care from your veterinarian for your breed of dog. Dogs that are prone to ear infections should be examined by the owner weekly (use treats and make it a good experience for the dog).

2. **Treatment A:** Temporary relief for your dog can be obtained by introducing a warm solution of water and white vinegar (50:50) into the ear by using a syringe. The dog must be prevented from shaking out the solution for a period of 1 minute. Gentle swabbing of the ear canal with cotton balls will remove debris.

   - Commercial preparations of ear cleaners are widely available and are balanced, slightly acidic solutions. These are not expensive and are recommended for your dog's medicine chest, especially for owners of water-loving dogs.

   - Overuse of ear cleaners can irritate your dog's ear. A rule of thumb is that if there is no improvement, after two cleanings, see the veterinarian.

   Treatment B: If ear mites are suspected (they look like coffee grounds in the ear), mineral oil or baby oil may bring temporary relief. See your vet ASAP, but please not in the middle of the night.

3. Dogs with large amounts of hair in the ear canal require either gentle teasing of the hair out of the ear canal or plucking of the hair out of the ear.

   - It is our opinion that, if the owner or groomer would like to "pluck" the hair from your dog's ear, he/she should do this on a regular basis (every 4 weeks). However, plucking the hair from a dirty ear or a mildly infected ear will make the condition worse. It is very common for an ear infection to "develop" after the yearly visit to the groomer. Don't blame the groomer.

   Authors' note: We are teasers, not "pluckers."

4. Dogs that are constantly in the water should be prevented from swimming until the ear infection has resolved. (Good luck on this suggestion.) Certain breeds require ongoing care and your vet will provide you with directions.

Eye Problems

ADULT DOGS
Possible Signs

- more than normal or greenish discharge from one or both eyes
- redness or cloudiness
- squinting or sensitivity to light
- rubbing of the eyes (pain)
- swelling of area around eyes
- excessive tearing

Problem Animals

- Dogs with pushed-in noses. These dogs have folds of skin beneath their eyes, and the hair covering these folds can touch the eye itself (e.g., bulldogs and shih tzus)
- Dogs with hairs (called *cilia*) on their eyelids that fold in and touch the eye (e.g., poodles)
- Dogs with eyelids that either roll into the eye (e.g., shar-pei) or droop too low (e.g., bloodhounds) and don't cover the eye

Summary

Eye problems are common in dogs. They range greatly in severity from the mildest case of excessive tearing, to an acute injury or serious infection. Due to the extreme differences in breeds, it is very important that you are aware of potential areas in which ongoing eye care is required. Ask your vet for advice with regards to your specific breed of dog.

Flushing the eye and the skin around the eye with warm water is the simplest and most effective form of eye care and emergency treatment. It is important never to ignore eye problems; an examination by your veterinarian and early treatment can save the eyesight of your dog. Older dogs can acquire age-related eye problems such as cataracts.

Eye Problems

ADULT DOGS

Has your dog been in an accident involving the eye? **YES** → Examine the eye for cause of damage; flush with water or contact lens solution and **CALL YOUR VET**

 NO

Is your dog a "problem breed"? **YES** → **CALL YOUR VET** Ask for suggestions on routine eye care for your breed of dog

 NO

Is one eye cloudy or larger than the other? **YES** → **CALL YOUR VET**

 NO

Is the area around the eye slowly swelling?
and/or
Does your dog have a history of bug bites? **YES** → See **BUG BITES AND REACTIONS**, page 65.
and/or
Does your dog have a history of allergies?

 NO

Is the eye severely painful or irritated? **YES** → Flush eye with water or contact lens solution and **CALL YOUR VET**

 NO

Is the eye mildly painful or irritated?

 YES

Flush eye with water or contact lens solution, and monitor closely.

Do not ignore eye problems; a chronic eye problem can result in severe damage to the eye. If you have any concerns, *CALL YOUR VET.*

Home Suggestions

1. Regular examinations of your dog's eyes will allow you to quickly identify problem areas. It is important to know what "normal" looks like.

2. Have your vet point out any areas that can potentially cause problems with your dog's eyes or the area around the eyes.

   - Dogs with flattened noses can have an excess amount of skin beneath the eyes. Hairs from the folds can touch the eyes causing excessive tearing that produces a "gunk" at the corners of the eyes.

     Clean these skin folds with warm water daily. This removes the gunk that builds up. (Make this daily care a good experience by giving the dog a treat after every wash.)

   - Other causes of eye gunk are problem eyelashes or problem eyelids. The treatment consists of daily washing with warm water.

3. Dogs that are rubbing their eyes or squinting require an immediate examination of the eye. If you cannot identify and correct the problem, see your vet. Dogs will cause more damage if they accidentally scratch their cornea.

   - Allergic reactions can sometimes cause swelling around the eyes or cause eye problems (redness and inflammation) directly. See the section on allergic reactions (page 65) for treatment.

4. An eye injury can be very serious. Examine the eye and flush with large amounts of water or contact lens solution. Flushing can remove a foreign body from the eye or it can dilute an irritating chemical like a shampoo. See your vet immediately if the condition does not resolve with flushing the eye.

5. Old dogs have more eye problems, and blindness is a common occurrence in dogs. Blind dogs do not need "guide people." Just don't move the furniture.

Skin Problems

ADULT DOGS
Possible Signs

- red or inflamed areas
- hair loss/change in skin color
- increased dandruff and shedding
- itchiness (scratching)
- open sores
- parasites visible (fleas, ticks, walking dandruff mites)

Summary

If you are looking for a quick solution to your dog's skin condition, you may be disappointed. Skin problems can be very frustrating to deal with, especially after the dog has scratched itself silly. Skin problems can be classified as bacterial/fungal/hormonal/parasitic/allergic and abnormal immune responses. Following a few simple suggestions can easily prevent some skin conditions; however, others may require veterinary assistance.

Skin Problems

ADULT DOGS

Is your dog showing other signs of illness?

or

Is your dog "scratching itself silly"?

YES **CALL YOUR VET**

 NO

Is there evidence of fleas, ticks, etc.?

YES See **ATTACK OF THE CRITTERS**, page 79, then return to this page.

 NO

Don't stop looking for critters; this is the number one cause of skin problems in dogs.

Are there small raw patches on your dog's skin (usually right by the tail)?

YES Try **HOT SPOT SUGGESTIONS**, page 60, then return to this page.

 NO

Is there evidence of blisters, ulcers, pus or large raw areas?

YES **CALL YOUR VET**

 NO

Is your dog's coat dry?

YES *use* **HOME SUGGESTIONS**

 NO

Is there evidence of mild skin irritation, itchiness or grooming problems?

YES *use* **HOME SUGGESTIONS**

 NO

Are there areas of hair loss (bald areas) or darkening of the skin (may indicate a possible hormonal problem)?

YES **CALL YOUR VET**

Home Suggestions

1. Proper grooming plays a large part in maintaining a healthy haircoat and skin, especially with certain breeds of dogs.
   - Non-shedding dogs should be clipped or brushed routinely to prevent mats from forming (e.g., poodles, shih tzus).
   - Dogs with heavy undercoats (the soft downy layer of fur) should have this hair removed to allow for the skin to "breathe," either by brushing or pulling at the coat (e.g., keeshonds).
   - Regular brushing should be done, especially in older or overweight dogs, both of which are unable to groom as well.
   - Breeds with extra skin require regular care of their "skin folds" (e.g., bulldogs, shar-pei). Daily washing with warm water followed by a thorough drying of the folds usually does the trick.

2. It is very important that the skin stays nice and dry in order to prevent bacterial infections from starting.
   - Make sure that your dog gets dried off after bathing or swimming, using either a towel or a hair dryer on low.
   - Keep the dog's collar off until your dog is dry to prevent extra moisture from getting trapped against the skin.
   - Keep higher-moisture areas clean and dry—between the toes, around the eyes and along the lips.

3. Contrary to popular belief, licking does not promote healing of sores. (If it were only that simple.) In some instances dogs will actually cause self-mutilation. In order to prevent licking, you can try some different ideas:
   - Use a piece of clothing to cover the sore, for example a T-shirt.
   - Create an at-home version of the "Elizabethan collar" using an ice cream pail or plastic bottle. Cut an area large enough for the dog's head to fit through snugly but not big enough so that the dog can easily slip its head out. Make sure you tape the cut edges of the pail to prevent irritation to the dog's neck. (This device looks very similar to a lamp shade or TV satellite dish on the head, and no, you will not get better reception while the dog is wearing it.)
   - Try a nasty-tasting spray that goes around the wound (e.g., **Bitter Apple**).

Tabasco sauce is **not** recommended. Using it may lead you to turn to the section on diarrhea (just a helpful hint).

4. Do not overbathe your dog. Shampooing strips the natural oils from the hair-coat, causing dandruff and itchiness. Use a dog shampoo and conditioner (not human shampoo or conditioner) to prevent a residue buildup on the dog's coat (Who wants limp hair?). Bathing the dog every 6 weeks is plenty unless medicated baths are required (e.g., tar-based shampoos for oily dogs and as indicated by your vet).

5. Make sure that your dog is on a good quality food. Not all brands are the same, and generally the lower the price tag the lower the quality of food. Low-quality dog foods tend to lack the essential fatty acids that the haircoat needs to remain healthy. Supplements that contain linolenic acids can also be used. Vegetable oil should only be used for dogs that do not have a weight problem.

6. Remember that dogs will get drier in the winter because of the drop in air humidity. Using a humidifier in your home will benefit both your dog and your family.

7. Allergies can cause a real problem, especially in the spring and summer months. Identifying the cause may be very difficult in most cases. An antihistamine will work in some dogs to help reduce generalized itchiness. Diphenhydramine (**Benadryl**) used at 2 mg per kg twice daily may do the trick—but always check with your vet.

8. Parasite control (see **Attack of the Critters**, page 79).

9. In the summer, "hot spots" or localized areas of infection occur frequently. The first step is to clip the hair close to the skin. Keep the area nice and clean using a diluted 3% peroxide solution, and make sure that the sore is kept dry.

A skin problem can be extremely frustrating for the owner and for the veterinarian. Proper grooming practices and attention to "critter control" solve many dog skin conditions. However, any dog may experience skin problems due to a variety of conditions, including hormonal problems, allergies, bacterial/fungal infections, etc. Be patient and understanding; solving this riddle can take a long time.

Sprains and Strains

ALL AGES
Possible Signs

- limping or abnormal gait
- non–weight bearing on any limb
- difficulty going up or down stairs
- pain or tenderness in the joints or muscles when touched

Summary

Sprains and strains are common injuries in dogs of all ages.

Puppies commonly are injured when the owners accidentally step on them or when they fall from a raised surface. The initial injury may recover fully within an hour. If the puppy is still limping after an hour, consult your veterinarian.

Adult dogs commonly have ligament sprains and muscle strains, typically after periods of excessive activity. This is the equivalent of the injuries sustained by "Weekend Warriors." (Can you relate to this one?) The seriousness of the injury can be further categorized by whether or not the dog is weight bearing/non–weight bearing on the limb. For a non–weight bearing injury that persists, see your vet immediately.

Treatment of injuries involves possible confinement to restrict activity and careful use of pain medication.

Home Suggestions

1. Accidents involving puppies are dramatic and tend to send their owners into a panic. Slow down and breathe deeply. Puppies are like children; there are a lot of tears and some pain but they tend to have a full recovery within an hour. If the lameness or pain persists or you do not feel comfortable with waiting, call your vet. Use common sense and treat the puppy as you would one of your own children. **Don't give painkillers to your puppy unless you have consulted your veterinarian.** Dosages vary and not all painkillers are meant for dogs.

2. If your adult dog has been out to the cottage for the first time this year and never stopped running and playing, it is easy to understand that it could be stiff and sore on Monday. Watch your pooch carefully and call your vet if recovery does not occur within another 24 hours.

3. Treatment of weight-bearing lameness in adult dogs includes restricted activity and ASA (**Aspirin** and others) in a dose (with food) of 10 mg per kg of body weight. Monitor closely and call your vet if the condition does not improve.

4. Non–weight bearing lameness in adult dogs should always be seen by a veterinarian, since your dog may have sustained broken bones and ruptured ligaments. This condition can be painful, so be careful when handling the animal and don't get bitten.

Bleeding Wounds

ALL AGES
Possible Signs

- although blood will be noted on your dog, it may be difficult to identify the source of the bleeding due to the hair covering the dog
- a cut pad will bleed profusely
- nails will bleed if cut too short
- bite wounds from other dogs are common sources of bleeding

Summary

A dog that is bleeding is very distressing to the owner. (To make matters worse, for minor wounds, dogs believe in bleeding throughout every room of your house. White carpets and beds are the first areas dogs will bleed on.)

Bleeding wounds are very common in dogs. Typical incidents include cut pads from stepping on glass, a dogfight and a nail that is cut too short by the owner.

The first step to examining your dog is to have someone you trust hold on to and control your pet's head. Remember, the wound might be painful, and when you touch it, your dog may bite. (Then we would have two bleeding wounds.)

The second step is to apply a clean cloth to the wound and apply direct pressure. Take a deep breath and calm down.

A cut nail bed will stop bleeding but may require assistance (see **Home Suggestions**). A cut pad or a bite wound should be seen by your veterinarian to determine if further treatment is required.

Home Suggestions

1. In dealing with an injured dog, you must:
   - Move slowly and be careful. DON'T GET BITTEN!
   - Talk softly and act calmly (your dog will sense your anxiety and become nervous).
   - It is advisable that someone holds and controls the head of the dog, while a second person performs the examination and administers treatment.
   - If you do not feel comfortable treating your pet, see your veterinarian.

2. Small abrasions and cuts can be treated with an antibiotic ointment (**Polysporin** and others). Clip the hair away and keep area clean. Apply 2 to 3 times daily.

3. Treatment of a bleeding nail due to an accident during nail trimming can be treated with a commercial product (**Quickstop** and others). Home products such as a bar of soap, cornstarch or flour can be applied with pressure to the end of the nail to assist in stopping the bleeding.

4. A veterinarian should examine bite wounds; a small puncture wound may cause more serious damage beneath the skin surface. Your veterinarian will assess the need for antibiotic therapy or surgery (stitches).

5. Applying direct pressure with a clean cloth, to a bleeding wound, will slow or stop the flow of blood.

Bug Bites and Allergic Reactions

ALL AGES
Possible Signs

Minor and localized

- pain, sudden crying or whining
- swelling
- redness on hairless parts of body (many bug bites appear as a red bull's-eye)

Major or severe reactions

- swelling of muzzle or head
- difficulty breathing
- crusting (scabbing), oozing lesions that spread beneath the fur

Summary

Most outside dogs will, at one time or another, have numerous fly bites on the hairless parts of their bodies, earflaps and bellies. If bites do not bother your dog, they typically disappear within 24 hours. Bug bites usually appear in the form of round red marks. A dog may infect bug bites by licking or scratching the area excessively.

Severe or major reactions may appear as localized or generalized swelling. Many dogs begin swelling on the nose or head, and the swelling can spread. If the dog's breathing becomes impaired or if it is in discomfort, see a veterinarian immediately.

Home Suggestions

1. Please refer to **Skin Problems in Puppies**, page 30, and **Skin Problems in Dogs**, page 57, for additional information.

2. The most common location for bee stings is on the head, neck or paw and within the mouth. A bee sting will be very painful initially. Occasionally, the dog owner will be able to see the "stinger" and it is possible to gently scrape the stinger free. A paste of baking soda and water over the area of discomfort provides almost immediate relief to the dog. (Thanks, Mom, for providing this tip, it works well.)

3. Some relief from insects can be obtained by using products like **Skin-So-Soft** or flea sprays. New products are becoming available, so contact your vet or ask at your local pet store. **Products containing "DEET" (an insect repellent) should not be used on dogs (they lick themselves, and this chemical is toxic).**

4. If your dog has had previous reactions, usually causing swelling of the head and neck, administer an antihistamine such as diphenhydramine (**Benadryl** and others) in a dose of 2 mg per kg of body weight—but talk to your vet first.

5. Local therapy for bug bites can involve the use of non-prescription or over-the-counter hydrocortisone cream or antihistamine. Prevent your dog from licking the cream for 10 minutes, to allow it time to work.

6. Mildly or superficially infected areas should be cleaned with an antibacterial soap and the hair removed from the area. Be gentle and move slowly, because treatment may be painful to your dog and the infected area may be larger than is visible. If in doubt, call your vet.

Dragging the Bum or "Scooting"

ALL AGES
Possible Signs

Minor

- dragging the bum across the carpet (usually in front of guests)
- terrible odor may be released from anal sacs

Major

- pain and swelling in area beneath the tail
- ruptured and draining abscess beneath the tail

Summary

"Scooting" is often reported by dog owners. It is most commonly caused by the dog being irritated by full or infected anal sacs. These sacs are located near the anus and are the same as the sacs that produce a skunk's smell. When the liquid from these sacs is released, there is a terrible odor. Release of this liquid is natural and is used by wild dogs for territorial marking.

Scooting is normal if it occurs infrequently—it is not a major concern, other than being a source of embarrassment. Daily or weekly scooting indicates that there may be a concern. Constant scooting is probably a sign of an abscessed sac.

Treatment may involve the draining or squeezing of these sacs or, occasionally, surgical intervention by a veterinarian.

Home Suggestions

1. Anal sacs should be drained or emptied by an experienced person. Squeezing the wrong way can result in damage to the structure of the sacs. Most wise people leave this job to the vet because it's gross.

2. A ruptured or abscessed anal sac must be treated by a veterinarian, but it does **not** have to be an after-hours emergency. Placing warm compresses (a clean, warm and wet cloth) gently beneath the tail will cleanse and comfort the dog.

Dental Disease

ALL AGES
Possible Signs

- tartar buildup is the most noticeable dental condition
- halitosis (bad breath)
- painful mouth (noticed by owner while petting the dog)
- difficulty eating or poor appetite
- occasionally, lethargy or depression (due to pain)

Summary

Dental disease is one of the most common conditions noticed in family dogs, and older pets are more prone to dental problems than their younger counterparts. The first sign of dental problems may be foul breath. Examination of the dog's teeth typically reveals tartar buildup near the gum line. Gingivitis, dental abscesses and a painful mouth can be signs of serious dental disease. Proper care includes daily brushing and regular professional care.

Puppies commonly have retained baby teeth. These teeth can cause crowding, which may lead to the entrapment of food particles. Retained baby teeth should be removed by your veterinarian (usually at the time of the neuter or spay).

Home Suggestions

1. Regular examination of your dog's mouth is an important aspect of dental health care.

2. To examine your dog's mouth, lift the outer lip flaps and look at all of the teeth including the molars. It is not necessary to pry open the mouth to examine the teeth (dogs hate that).

3. Regular brushing of your pet's teeth will slow down tartar buildup and prevent dental disease. Use a toothpaste recommended by your veterinarian.

4. Treats are available that help keep tooth and dental disease under control. Ask your vet about these.

5. It is important to have your dog's teeth examined by a veterinarian, in order to determine if professional care is required.

Starting a daily teeth brushing program for your dog:

The Hotdog Method

1. For two weeks give your dog a small piece of a hotdog (cold wiener) at the same time each day. This will set your dog's internal clock to expect a treat at this time every day.

2. Starting in the third week, "brush" the dog's teeth with the piece of hotdog and then give the dog the hotdog as a treat. Perform this ritual for 1 week.

3. The next week use a wet cloth or finger-cot toothbrush to wipe the dog's teeth. Ensure that you give the hotdog treat after you clean the teeth.

4. After the dog has become accustomed to this daily ritual, you can add doggy toothpaste. Don't use human toothpaste, as it contains fluoride and it also tends to foam up. Remember, dogs don't know how to spit.

5. Don't try to brush the inside of the teeth. Stick to the outside surfaces. Be gentle but firm and stand to the side of the dog when brushing.

Things to Avoid

If you believe that your dog has just eaten something toxic, contact your veterinarian immediately. Time is an important factor in all cases of poisoning. Don't wait and see.

Chocolate Toxicity

"My dog likes to eat what I eat!" Sure dogs like to eat chocolate, but what they like to eat and what is good for them are two totally different things. We are not talking about putting on a few extra pounds or getting a few pimples; chocolate may cause stomach upset, severe diarrhea hyperactivity and even death in dogs. Most people don't realize chocolate contains chemicals that can severely harm or kill their pets. Obviously the amount and the type of chocolate product eaten determines the severity of the signs shown by the dog. Cocoa beans, for example, would top the list as being the most dangerous, followed by baking chocolate, then milk chocolate, chocolate drinks and finally white chocolate. Did you know that as little as half of a cup of chocolate milk could kill a 5-pound (2.25 kg) dog? Yes, believe it or not 5-pound (2.25 kg) dogs do exist! So next Easter or Halloween, remember to hide that extra stash of chocolate, to prevent both the kids and the dog from bouncing off the walls. *Lethal dose: 0.25 oz (7 g) of baking chocolate or 2 oz (56 g) milk chocolate per kilogram of body weight.*

Antifreeze Toxicity

Some dogs like antifreeze because it is sweet, and a very small amount can quickly lead to vomiting, depression, seizuring and even death. As little as 2 tsp (10 mL) of antifreeze can actually kill a small dog. The chemical (ethylene glycol) contained within antifreeze does not only cause the initial signs described above, but can also be broken down into a type of crystal that can lead to kidney failure up to a week later. It is therefore very important to keep these products in sealed containers away from animal contact and to clean up after working on vehicles. Even if dogs do not directly lick antifreeze from a spill, they can still ingest some while doing regular grooming if any has collected on their haircoat.

> *Sunlight dish detergent works well to remove antifreeze and oil products from a dog's haircoat.*

A small amount of antifreeze can be very harmful to your dog's health. If you suspect a possible ingestion, **CALL YOUR VET** immediately.

Mouse and Rat Poison

Why would any dog eat mouse or rat poison? These products often have an appealing candy-like appearance; however, in most cases, dogs eat them simply because they are there. You can purchase tons of different products that will kill mice and rats, but the most popular are those that contain "anticoagulants." These interfere with regular blood clotting, causing the victim to bleed to death in most circumstances. Unfortunately the victim is not always the mouse. In dogs the effects of the poison will usually not be seen for a number of days. Secondary poisonings are also possible, meaning that if Fido eats the mice that have been killed by the poison, he can also be in trouble. If you suspect your dog has eaten mouse or rat poison, be on the safe side and contact your veterinarian immediately. If the animal is going in to the clinic to be treated, bring the box or container that the mouse or rat poison came in, so that the veterinarian has a better idea of what he/she is dealing with.

Bones

Just because your parents did it and their parents before them...! Bones can cause a lot of damage to your dog. This includes all forms of bones, not just chicken bones as we often hear. Many people think that bones take tartar off their dogs' teeth, but as the tartar comes off so can large chunks of a tooth.

Sharp pieces of bones also cause a lot of damage to your dog's stomach and intestines because bones cannot be digested. Dogs that have eaten bones can suffer from vomiting and bloody diarrhea, as well as constipation in some cases. Can you imagine the pain of trying to pass those sharp pieces of bone? The main concern is the possibility that pieces of bone blocking the intestines can lead to death if the dog is not treated surgically by a veterinarian. Although most dogs will never have a problem with bones in their lifetime, not giving them any at all is a guaranteed way to ensure that your dog is not one of the unlucky ones. Stick with nylon bones or raw hide bones—they are much safer for your pet.

Riding in the Back of a Truck— Don't Do It!

Some people cannot imagine their dogs (one of their family members) riding in the back of a truck. Unfortunately, veterinarians all too often deal with dogs that have fallen from these vehicles. Dogs are curious creatures and have been known to jump out of a moving truck if something more interesting passes by. Injuries usually include anything from cuts to broken bones. Even well-trained dogs that don't jump from the vehicle can easily be thrown with a quick or sudden turn. Many people believe they have solved the problem by attaching the dog by a chain to the box of the truck. Strangulation could happen if the chain is too long and the dog is able to get part of its body over the side of the vehicle. We must also remember that a dog riding in the back of a truck is exposed to all that the outside world has to offer, including wind, rain, dust and flying insects. So next time you see a dog with runny red eyes and bugs in its teeth, you will know how it travels.

Giving Our Medication to Our Pets

We don't use our pet's medication, so why are we quick to use our medications on our pets? Most medications used in human and veterinary medicine are similar, but caution should be taken—checking with a veterinarian is advisable. There are several reasons for concern:

1. We have no way of knowing if we are using the appropriate medication for the dog's condition.

2. Humans and animals break down drugs differently in their bodies. The amount used on a 130-lb (58.5 kg) Great Dane could be very different than the amount used on a person of the same size.

3. We need to remember the great variation in the body sizes of dogs—they can range from 5 lbs (2.25 kg) to 175 lbs (78.8 kg). Therefore, when treating your pet with medications, forget the saying "one size fits all." Remember to keep these things in mind before reaching for the drug cabinet, and call the vet first.

Heatstroke

Dogs are unable to sweat through their skin; therefore, they may quickly become overheated in certain situations. Dogs regulate their body temperature by sweating through glands in their footpads and by panting. Heatstroke can happen in a variety of situations. Here are some suggestions for prevention, detection and early treatment of heatstroke.

Prevention: "If it is too hot for you, then it is too hot for your dog."
- provide a good supply of cool water to drink
- provide some sort of shade
- some dogs love to swim to stay cool; filling a small child's pool would do the trick
- keep activity to a minimum during the hottest part of the day, and take the dog for a walk once it has cooled down in the evening, or early in the morning
- in summer, **never** leave dogs unattended inside cars, even for just a few minutes

> *Dogs with "pushed-in" noses (e.g., bulldogs) are more prone to heatstroke. Dogs can also suffer from heatstroke in the winter, when left in a car with the heater on full blast.*

Detection:

- excessive panting, increased salivation, trouble breathing, a seizure or collapse

Early Treatment:

- get the dog out of the heat
- attempt to cool its body temperature by placing it in a cool (not freezing) bath
- rubbing alcohol can be rubbed on the dog's footpads to help with heat loss
- use the breeze from an electric fan to cool down your dog

> *Dogs that are not responding to the treatment, showing difficulty breathing or have experienced a seizure should be examined by a veterinarian.*

Strange Things
Dogs Do

Eating Grass

Contrary to belief, dogs do not usually eat grass when they feel ill and want to make themselves sick. In fact, most dogs actually seem to enjoy eating grass. Some believe that this behavior is driven by an instinctive need for greenery in their diet, since wild dogs used to eat all of their grass-eating prey, including stomach contents. Although grass eating is not an offensive behavior, it can lead to several problems, such as vomiting, and constipation if it is taken in large quantities. Grass eating should be limited because the dog may also be ingesting eggs on the grass from several kinds of intestinal worms. Another concern is the danger of poisoning from pesticide use on lawns. Make sure your dog has lots of toys and playtime—some dogs eat grass when bored.

Eating Poop

A large number of dogs will eat just about anything. Sometimes, the more offensive to us, the better it tastes to them. Some dogs even eat poop. Upsetting to us as dog owners, this practice is not that far off from some of their natural behaviors. As dogs groom themselves, they clean everywhere, including the rectal area. Mother dogs clean the rectal area of their puppies to stimulate them to poop, at the same time eating the fecal material to keep their living area clean.

Why do dogs eat poop? Theories include:

- boredom
- parasite infections that lead to increased appetite
- something is lacking in the dog's diet
- it just tastes good—some dogs prefer frozen poop, known as "poopsicles" Authors' note: No one in the vet profession has seen fit to verify this explanation.

In order to eliminate some of these possibilities a "fecal" can be run at a veterinary clinic on some of the dog poop (if the dog has not already eaten it all) to rule out parasites as a cause. Increasing the dog's regular activity as well as regularly changing its toys can eliminate boredom. A dog's diet can easily be changed or supplements can be added. Try to reduce access to any poop by cleaning the yard regularly and placing litter boxes out of reach. Keep your dog on a leash and clean up poop immediately, or the act of eating it will reinforce the vice. There are products available, such as **Forbid**, that when added to the dog's diet will change form following digestion into a bitter-tasting substance in their poop. (This product comes from the manufacturer's anti-coprophagic division—a scientific term for anti-poop eating division. We think this is pretty funny.) Sometimes **Clorets** or **Certs** breathmints help, too. Mix one in with the dog's food; it makes the dog's stool taste funny.

Twitching While Sleeping– All Animals Dream

A lot of dog owners are concerned when they witness their dog twitching and whining while it is asleep. In most cases the dog is just dreaming. They are reacting to the thoughts that are going through their mind. This is a normal process and it is not necessary to wake the dog up each time you see this happening. (Remember that we do not appreciate it when our dogs wake us up, so we are assuming that they do not like it when we wake them up.)

Seizures can produce some similar activities, but usually begin when the dog is awake and moving around. Seizures are typically more vigorous and most animals can not be "awakened" while they are in progress. Monitor your dog closely, and if you are concerned, contact your veterinarian.

Choking or Snorting Episodes

At one time or another most dog owners have experienced their dog "reverse sneezing." A reverse sneeze involves the movement of air in and out of the throat area. It has been described by owners as sounding like an asthma attack or a choking episode. It usually lasts for only seconds, but can be scary for somebody who is hearing it for the first time. By calming the dog down and gently rubbing its throat, the condition usually subsides. Reverse sneezing occurs more frequently in certain breeds, and it is typically not treated unless increased irritation of the throat (e.g., virus) is causing it to occur more frequently.

Hiccuping

If you have a puppy you will more than likely hear it hiccup again and again. Regardless of the cause, hiccuping is considered a normal part of a puppy's life and they are not unhealthy in any way because of it. like humans, adult dogs will also still hiccup occasionally, and too much beer does not necessarily cause it.

Housesoiling

Most dogs are very clean and have a natural tendency to keep their living area free of poop and pee. However, they require training during the puppy stage to ensure that housetraining is achieved and maintained throughout their lives.

Puppy Training Hints:

- Establish regular patterns in your puppy's daily schedule and try to be consistent. Take him outside frequently.
- Feed him on a schedule and take him outside immediately after eating and drinking. What goes in comes out; it is a natural reflex.
- Only discipline if you catch him in the act. I know he looks guilty, but he really doesn't know why you are mad at him. Don't rub his nose in it. This approach to discipline may encourage him to eat his poop when he gets older. Besides, the practice is disgusting.
- Be patient.
- Praise him when he pees and poops outside (praise works much better than punishment).

Older dogs that begin to soil in the house often have a medical problem. **CALL YOUR VET**. The answer to the problem can often be solved quickly with the correct medical management. Don't give up on your older pet too soon. Sometimes, like people, they get forgetful and need to be reminded where the bathroom is.

Attack of the
Critters

Skunk Spray

When you least expect it, it happens. The friendly neighborhood skunk decides to spray your precious Fido. What can you do? Try these suggestions.

1. Mix 4 cups (1 L) of 3 percent hydrogen peroxide, 1/4 cup (60 mL) baking soda and 1 tsp (5 mL) liquid soap. Apply to the dog when it is dry to help break down the oils that make up the smelly spray. Wash the dog well afterward with a dog shampoo.

2. You can try the old traditional tomato-juice bath; it seems to help.

3. There are now several products on the market specific to this problem, such as **Skunk Off.**

4. Contact lens solution can also come in handy to flush your dog's eyes if he gets skunk spray square in the face. The strong spray can actually burn the surface of the eye if it makes direct contact (chemical burn).

Porcupine Quills

Yes it is true: dogs do not learn from their mistakes. No matter how much pain the quills from a porcupine cause, dogs will keep going back for more. There are a few things that you should know about quills:

1. Pieces of broken-off quills can migrate through the tissue for weeks, even months, afterward; therefore, check the dog's body regularly to try to find any remnants. Run your hands through the fur, and when you get poked, you've found one.

2. Quills should not be cut before being pulled; this does not make it easier to remove them and can actually be more time consuming and painful for the dog. (It also makes the vet really angry.)

3. Remember that the dog is in pain. Be patient and be careful.

4. Quills can be pulled from the skin using needle-nosed pliers. If there are quills in the dog's mouth or a large number in the dog's body, call your veterinarian.

5. Clean the dog's skin with a disinfectant for several days following removal in order to prevent infection. (Ask your vet for the type of disinfectant to use.)

Fleas

Just the word "fleas" sends shivers through most people's bodies. People dread having to try to treat the problem.

Fleas have 4 stages to their life cycle: eggs (pearly white < 1/2 mm long), pupa (found in a soft cocoon, up to 4 mm long), larva (segmented wormlike body) and the adult (wingless, brown, 4 mm long). Eggs are laid on a host (the dog) and then fall into the surroundings. One flea can lay more than 2,000 eggs. Larvae will develop in areas that are secluded and dark (e.g., in carpets, on basement floors). More larvae will be found in "source spots," where the dog spends the most time. The time it takes to develop from an egg to an adult is, on average, 1 month; however, it can range from 9 days to 20 months depending on conditions (temperature, humidity). Adult fleas can only survive 2 to 4 days off the host, whereas their lifespan is about 3 months on the host.

Here are some suggestions for controlling these critters:

1. Clean the house. Wash pet bedding, vacuum and mop areas thoroughly, making sure to throw the sealed vacuum bag away outside after you are done.

2. Spray the house. Focus on "source spots" first. Then treat anyplace that the dog can go, including areas like the car. An alternative is to have a pest extermination company fumigate your home.

3. Treat all the animals in the house. Caution should be taken with cats because they are more sensitive to flea products; re-treatment may be required. There are lots of new products available for flea prevention and treatment—make sure to ask your veterinarian about them. Some people believe that feeding their dogs garlic and brewer's yeast will help to repel fleas. This strategy may work for some dogs but not all. Please note: always read the directions on flea spray; house sprays are not meant to be used on pets.

Ticks

These little guys seem to like to catch a ride and a meal at the same time. The visible part of a tick is their grayish saclike body (1/4 to 1/2 cm) that protrudes from your dog's skin while its mouth parts are buried in the tissue. In some parts of the world ticks are known for spreading diseases. To most owners, however, the irritation that ticks cause to their dogs is of more concern.

Before removing the tick, try to reduce its hold by applying either mineral oil or rubbing alcohol around its body. Gently grasp the tick with tweezers as close to the skin surface as possible and pull. You will probably hear a popping noise as it releases. Make sure you have removed the entire body and mouthpiece. The skin is usually quite inflamed for several days following tick removal, therefore the area should be kept disinfected in order to prevent a secondary infection. There are numerous products that are available to prevent your dog from getting ticks—ask your veterinarian. If your dog runs in wooded areas, make sure to do regular "tick checks."

Health Record

Pet's Name: _____   Date Born: _____

Breed: _____   Sex: _____

Where Acquired: _____

Record of Shots:

Date	Type	Date	Type

Emergency Information

(If you're leaving your pet in the care of someone else, make sure they have this information.)

Vet: _____   Phone: _____

Address: _____

_____

Insurance Company: _____   Phone: _____

Policy Number: _____   Representative: _____

Coverage: _____

Whenever you're talking with your vet about a problem, you should be able to give the vet a specific description of the problem including:

- how long it's lasted,
- how your pet is behaving,
- what the symptoms are,
- what you think the cause is.

Have a pen or pencil ready to take notes.

Health History

Date:_____

Problem: _____

_____

_____

Veterinarian Recommendations: _____

_____

_____

_____

Date:_____

Problem: _____

_____

_____

Veterinarian Recommendations: _____

_____

_____

_____

Date:_____

Problem: _____

_____

_____

Veterinarian Recommendations: _____

_____

_____

_____

Date:_____

Problem: _____

_____

_____

Veterinarian Recommendations: _____

_____

_____

_____

Date:_____

Problem: _____

_____

_____

Veterinarian Recommendations: _____

_____

_____

_____

Date:_____

Problem: _____

_____

_____

Veterinarian Recommendations: _____

_____

_____

_____

Date:_____

Problem: _____

_____

_____

Veterinarian Recommendations: _____

_____

_____

_____

Date:_____

Problem: _____

_____

_____

Veterinarian Recommendations: _____

_____

_____

_____

Date:_____

Problem: _____

_____

_____

Veterinarian Recommendations: _____

_____

_____

_____

Date:_____

Problem: _____

_____

_____

Veterinarian Recommendations: _____

_____

_____

_____

Date:_____

Problem: _____

_____

_____

Veterinarian Recommendations: _____

_____

_____

_____

Date:_____

Problem: _____

_____

_____

Veterinarian Recommendations: _____

_____

_____

_____

Date:_____

Problem: _____

_____

_____

Veterinarian Recommendations: _____

_____

_____

_____

Date:_____

Problem: _____

_____

_____

Veterinarian Recommendations: _____

_____

_____

_____

Date:_____

Problem: _____

_____

_____

Veterinarian Recommendations: _____

_____

_____

_____